Reversing Wegener's Granulomatosis Naturally

The Raw Vegan Plant-Based Detoxification & Regeneration Workbook for Healing Patients.

Volume 2

Health Central

Copyright © 2019

Welcome to Healing

"Let food be thy medicine and medicine be thy food."

- Hippocrates

We want to deliver you the maximum benefit in the shortest time so we have compiled notes alongside a tried and tested healing protocol that we discovered through our work with a variety of individuals including Wegener's Granulomatosis patients.

The aim is to increase your internal Oxygen levels, alkalize your body, cleanse your digestive and lymphatic systems (and blood) whilst increasing your absorption and energy levels. Good health will soon follow.

As we know, all species originally ate raw. Fruit was the food intended for our (Fruigivore) species. Our evolution into eating cooked foods has lead to today's "disease" crisis. Cooked/low energy foods (mainly animal and starch based) hinder healing and create the perfect environment for sickness to exist.

An internal alkaline environment on the other hand (achieved mainly through fruits) repels disease, suffering and pain, whilst encouraging healing and regeneration.

Having healed numerous patients – we have arrived at a series of conclusions and treatment protocols:

1. Regardless of the labelled "condition" or "disease" – the obstruction of an internal acidic environment can be corrected. If your car has an oil leak, you don't just stick a plaster over the leak. Instead you find the root cause and repair this. Similarly we want to correct our root issues to achieve lasting results.

2. In simple terms, "dis-ease" within the body stems from internal congestion resulting from the sustained consumption of acid-forming (cooked) foods which the body struggles to process, but over time just gets on with it.

3. Our lymphatic system is responsible for washing our blood but when it has become stagnant/un-responsive, the acids just continue to slowly pile up in our blood. With our organs now surrounded by "un-washed" blood, dis-ease begins.

4. For us to activate our lymphatic system, we need to initiate filtration of our skin and kidneys (your skin being the 3rd kidney and

largest eliminative organ – through sweat). Regular bowel movements also support the detoxification process. The combination of herbs, dry fasting and eating/juicing fruit will regulate these systems.

5. Sleep is important and allows for recovery. We advise patients to sleep from 10pm every night and awaken when it feels natural to do so. Be sure to stop all eating by early evening so your body can start to wind down and prepare for sleep.

6. Dry fasting (nil by mouth) eliminates toxins and weak cells that are not performing at their best. Intermittent fasting has helped many patients achieve positive results. Dry fast until as late as possible into the day before eating a fruit that additionally has a laxative effect (e.g. prunes, plums, grapes, figs, oranges). This process will help flush out the fast's accumulated toxins. **Note:** after a long dry fast, a "laxative fruit" is necessary because fasts can cause constipation.

7. Long dry fasts do yield great results but they can be harsh on your adrenal glands (stressful) so we advise taking adrenal glandulars and liquorice root to support them. The longer you can dry fast, whilst limiting your eating window, the better the results will be. However, you must work up to this. Do not just jump in with a long dry fast, especially if you have weak kidneys / adrenal glands. Start by having a delayed fruit breakfast, working towards skipping breakfast altogether, to having only 1 fruit meal in the day. **Always** work at your own pace and listen to your body.

Critical Notes: Fruit coupled with fasting will expose your weaknesses so you will need to be prepared for this. Your body will eliminate all past illnesses that may have been suppressed with allopathic medicines, along with other toxic loads. This can be quite an experience so having the appropriate supplementation in place to support your detox is crucial. Taking glandulars and specific herbs is recommended for all pre-existing weaknesses.

Iridology Session: We can identify your weaknesses and areas to focus on through an Iridology (Iris Diagnosis) session. Each person is different and the eyes help us to identify how to best support each patient individually.

To book a session, email us at HealingCentral8@gmail.com. We tend to perform iris reads on all patients before starting to work with them – this is an important investigative step.

8. The goal is to work up towards completing 7 consecutive days of fruit fasting (it becomes significantly easier from this point on) and then to 14 days, 30 days, and so on.

9. As parasites and various other toxic elements die off, you may experience certain symptoms. One common symptom is extreme food cravings (for starchy, meaty, cheesy foods) – but do not be fooled, this is not YOU craving, it is just the parasites trying to pull you back down and resisting your cleansing attempts. You could take some parasite cleansing herbs (CureMyParasite.com) to aide their removal.

10. Fruit (e.g. melons, berries, grapes, citrus) with the rich fructose content will be your main food during your detoxification period. For the deepest detox experience, slow juice your fruits and stick with a single fruit throughout (grape juice alone has given us the best results – oranges are also very impressive).

11. Juicing allows for accelerated results (your body can focus all of its energy on healing as opposed to digestion). Specific herbs (e.g. Cleavers, Manjistha, Parsley, Cilantro) will enhance detoxification. Vegetables tend to slow down the detoxification process, while starches, nuts/seeds, legumes, and cooked foods will halt the detoxification process.

Note: Proteins, dairy, and grain-based foods will reverse your detoxification progress so these foods need to be eliminated from your diet.

12. Dried fruits (dates, figs, apricots, bananas, avocados) can be used to assist if you are feeling empty or struggling with cravings in the initial stages. However, do get back onto water dense fresh/tree-ripened fruit (watermelons/melons, berries, oranges, and grapes being the preferred kind) as soon as possible (ideally juiced). A list of detox-proven fruits can be found in the following point.

13. Examples of fruits proven to offer reliable detoxification:

Apples, Apricots, Blueberries, Blackberries, Cherries, Clementines, Figs, Tangerines, Lemons, Limes, Grapefruit, Mango, Grapes, Strawberries, Raspberries, Oranges, Pomegranates, Pineapples, Plums, Pears, Prunes, Watermelon

14. It is important that your body is absorbing correctly otherwise deficiencies can ensue. We have found most patients to be suffering from malabsorption – this is confirmed through the iris.

15. If you are on medications, work with your Medical Doctor (MD) and have regular blood work done so your personal progress can be monitored. Positive results will occur within a short timeframe so do pay close attention to your state and remember to reduce medication if no longer required. We also recommend tracking your progress through an Iridology session every 6 to 12 months. This shows us which areas are resolving and those that need continued work.

Our goal throughout this workbook is to help you with recording your progress and applying the information stated in the above points.

Start with what you are most comfortable with and make it enjoyable, choose your favourite sweet fruits. If a client deviates from the routine, we advise to get back on track as soon as possible. Just keep moving forward, keep track of progress, and be persistent.

We would like to wish you all the best and if you would like to book a consultation, or if you have any questions, thoughts, or comments, feel free to email us at:

HealingCentral8@gmail.com

Good Luck with your healing journey.

Tried & Tested Fruit Juicer: **YourFruitJuicer.com**

Tried & Tested Vegetable Juicer: **YourVegJuicer.com**

Got Meaty/Starchy/Cheesy Food Cravings?

CureMyParasite.com

[EXAMPLE 1]
Today's Date: 2nd Jan 2019

Morning

I just ate 3 mangoes – very sweet and tasty. I felt a heavy feeling under my chest area so I stopped eating. Unsure what that was - maybe digestive or the transverse colon?

Afternoon

I was feeling hungry so I am eating some dried figs, pineapple and apricots with around 750ml of spring water.

Evening

Sipping on a green tea (herbal). Feeling pretty strong and alert at the moment.

Night

Enjoying a bowl of red seeded grapes. Currently I feel satisfied.

Today's Notes (Highlights, Thoughts, Feelings):

Unlike yesterday, today was a good day. I am noticing an increase in regular bowel movements which makes me feel cleansed and light afterwards. I feel as though my kidneys are also starting to filter better (white sediment visible in morning wee).

It definitely helps to document my thoughts in this workbook. A great way to reflect, improve and stay on track.

Feeling very good – vibrant and strong – I have noticed a major improvement in my physical fitness and performance. Mentally I feel healthier and happier.

[EXAMPLE 2]
Today's Date: 3rd Jan 2019

Morning

Dry fasting (water and food free since 8pm last night) - will go up until 12:30pm today, and start with 500ml of spring water before eating half a watermelon.

Afternoon

Kept busy and was in and out quite a bit – so nothing consumed.

Evening

At around 5pm, I had a peppermint tea with a selection of mixed dried fruit (small bowl of apricot, dates, mango, pineapple, and prunes).

Night

Sipped on spring water through the evening as required.
Finished off the other half of the watermelon from the morning.

Today's Notes (Highlights, Thoughts, Feelings):

As with most days, today started well with me dry fasting (continuing my fast from my sleep/skipping breakfast) up until around 12:30pm and then eating half a watermelon. The laxative effect of the watermelon helped me poop and release any loosened toxins from the fasting period.
I tend to struggle on some days from 3pm onwards. Up until that point I am okay but if the cravings strike then it can be challenging. I remind myself that those burgers and chips do not have any live healing energy.
I feel good in general. I feel fantastic doing a fruit/juice fast but slightly empty by the end of the day.
Cooked food makes me feel severe fatigue and mental fog.
Will continue with my fruit fasting and start to introduce fruit juices due to their deeper detox benefits. I would love to be on juices only as I have seen others within the community achieve amazing results.

[EXAMPLE 3]

Today's Date: 4th Jan 2019

Morning

Today I woke and my children were enjoying some watermelon for breakfast – and the smell was luring so I joined them. Large bowl of watermelon eaten at around 8am. Started with a glass of water.

Afternoon

Snacked on left over watermelon throughout the morning and afternoon. Had 5 dates an hour or so after.

Evening

Had around 3 mangoes at around 6pm. Felt content – but then I was invited round to a family gathering where a selection of pizzas, burgers and chips were being served. I gave into the peer pressure and felt like I let myself down!

Night

Having over-eaten earlier on in the evening, I was still feeling bloated with a headache (possibly digestion related) and I also felt quite mucus filled (wheez in chest and coughing up phlegm). Very sleepy and low energy. The perils of cooked foods!!

Today's Notes (Highlights, Thoughts, Feelings):

I let myself down today. It all started well until I ate a fully blown meal (and over-ate). I didn't remain focussed and I spun off track. As a result my energy levels were much lower and I felt a bout of extreme fatigue 30 minutes after the meal (most likely the body struggling to with digesting all that cooked food).
I need to stick to the plan because the difference between fruit fasting, and eating cooked foods is huge – 1 makes you feel empowered whilst the other makes you feel drained. I also felt the mucus overload after the meal – it kicked in pretty quickly.
Today I felt disappointed after giving in to the meal but tomorrow is a new day and I will keep on going! It is important to remind myself that I won't get better if I cannot stick to the routine.

Frequently Asked Questions

Are avocados okay to eat on this protocol?

They are perfectly fine during the transition period (when moving over from cooked foods to a fruit diet). Bananas, dates and figs are another recommendation of ours. You can also make a number of tasty salads or pastas (with Zucchini/Courgette) during this period. However do keep in mind that they do not hold much detoxification value, so they should be used sparingly.

How long is the healing period - when will I be healed?

This depends on how well your body responds, how congested you were to start with – in short, a number of factors will contribute to how quickly you are able to heal. Everybody is different, some patients have had success within 30 days, whilst others have seen positive results within 60 days. Note: this is a long-term journey and we don't advise looking at timeframes but instead to focus on the positive changes that you experience - it is meant to be a lifestyle change. The rest will be down to you to decide – i.e. either continue with the routine that allows for you to feel this wonderful, or go back to low-energy foods that create fatigue and dis-ease within the body.

Can I go back to eating cooked foods?

Once you have healed and have a regular fruit routine going - if you still have a desire for a specific cooked meal, then I would say an occasional "Treat Day" wouldn't be the end of the world. However with time, you will notice a change in the foods that you desire so listen to your body. Note: certain cravings can stem from parasites so we tend to recommend supplementing with the herbal parasite formula found on this link: **CureMyParasite.com**

Some say juicing is not good for the body – is this true?

Everybody will have different opinions so we focus on what has proven to work and achieve results. We have found juicing to be highly beneficial and patients have experienced accelerated results. Juice will deliver all of the nutrients to your body, limiting fermentation, and digestion energy. This energy will be directed towards your healing. Ensure you are drinking a sufficient amount of juice in order to receive the best level of nutrition for yourself. Everybody is unique and will have different requirements. So if you feel like you want more juice - keep juicing, but most importantly, listen to your body at all times.

Today's Date:

Morning
(work towards continuing your night time dry fast up until at least 12pm)

Afternoon
(get hydrating with fresh fruit or even better slow juiced fruits/berries/melons)

Evening
(aim to wind down to a dry fast by around 6pm to 7pm)

Night
(work your way up to dry fasting from the evening until 12pm the following day)

Today's Notes (Highlights, Thoughts, Feelings, What Could You Improve On?)

"Get yourself an accountability partner to complete a 3 month detox with.
Start with 7 days and work your way up.
It will be fun and motivating completing it with somebody (or a group) ...or of course you can go it alone"

Today's Date:

Morning
(work towards continuing your night time dry fast up until at least 12pm)

Afternoon
(get hydrating with fresh fruit or even better slow juiced fruits/berries/melons)

Evening
(aim to wind down to a dry fast by around 6pm to 7pm)

Night
(work your way up to dry fasting from the evening until 12pm the following day)

Today's Notes (Highlights, Thoughts, Feelings, What Could You Improve On?)

"Remember to keep yourself hydrated with water too (spring water preferred)."

Today's Date:

Morning

(work towards continuing your night time dry fast up until at least 12pm)

Afternoon

(get hydrating with fresh fruit or even better slow juiced fruits/berries/melons)

Evening

(aim to wind down to a dry fast by around 6pm to 7pm)

Night

(work your way up to dry fasting from the evening until 12pm the following day)

14

Today's Notes (Highlights, Thoughts, Feelings, What Could You Improve On?)

"Eat melons/watermelons separately, and before any other fruit as it digests faster and we want to limit fermentation (acidity) which can occur if other fruits are mixed in."

Today's Date:

Morning
(work towards continuing your night time dry fast up until at least 12pm)

Afternoon
(get hydrating with fresh fruit or even better slow juiced fruits/berries/melons)

Evening
(aim to wind down to a dry fast by around 6pm to 7pm)

Night
(work your way up to dry fasting from the evening until 12pm the following day)

**Today's Notes (Highlights, Thoughts, Feelings, What Could
You Improve On?)**

*"Stay focussed on the end goal of removing
mucus & toxins from your body and feeling
wonderful again!"*

Today's Date:

Morning

(work towards continuing your night time dry fast up until at least 12pm)

Afternoon

(get hydrating with fresh fruit or even better slow juiced fruits/berries/melons)

Evening

(aim to wind down to a dry fast by around 6pm to 7pm)

Night

(work your way up to dry fasting from the evening until 12pm the following day)

Today's Notes (Highlights, Thoughts, Feelings, What Could You Improve On?)

"Meditate and perform deep breathing exercises in order to help yourself remain present minded and stay on track."

Today's Date:

Morning

(work towards continuing your night time dry fast up until at least 12pm)

Afternoon

(get hydrating with fresh fruit or even better slow juiced fruits/berries/melons)

Evening

(aim to wind down to a dry fast by around 6pm to 7pm)

Night

(work your way up to dry fasting from the evening until 12pm the following day)

Today's Notes (Highlights, Thoughts, Feelings, What Could You Improve On?)

"Join a few like-minded communities – there are many juicing and raw vegan based groups, both online and offline. Being part of a community can help motivate you to reach your goals."

Today's Date:

Morning
(work towards continuing your night time dry fast up until at least 12pm)

Afternoon
(get hydrating with fresh fruit or even better slow juiced fruits/berries/melons)

Evening
(aim to wind down to a dry fast by around 6pm to 7pm)

Night
(work your way up to dry fasting from the evening until 12pm the following day)

Today's Notes (Highlights, Thoughts, Feelings, What Could You Improve On?)

"If you are struggling with hunger pangs in the early stages, try some dates or dried apricots, prunes, or raisins, with a cup of herbal tea.

Today's Date:

Morning
(work towards continuing your night time dry fast up until at least 12pm)

Afternoon
(get hydrating with fresh fruit or even better slow juiced fruits/berries/melons)

Evening
(aim to wind down to a dry fast by around 6pm to 7pm)

Night
(work your way up to dry fasting from the evening until 12pm the following day)

Today's Notes (Highlights, Thoughts, Feelings, What Could You Improve On?)

"Get into a routine of regularly buying fresh fruit (or grow your own if weather permits) to keep your supplies up."

Today's Date:

Morning

(work towards continuing your night time dry fast up until at least 12pm)

Afternoon

(get hydrating with fresh fruit or even better slow juiced fruits/berries/melons)

Evening

(aim to wind down to a dry fast by around 6pm to 7pm)

Night

(work your way up to dry fasting from the evening until 12pm the following day)

Today's Notes (Highlights, Thoughts, Feelings, What Could You Improve On?)

"Regularly remind yourself about the great rewards and benefits that you will experience from keeping up this detox."

Today's Date:

Morning

(work towards continuing your night time dry fast up until at least 12pm)

Afternoon

(get hydrating with fresh fruit or even better slow juiced fruits/berries/melons)

Evening

(aim to wind down to a dry fast by around 6pm to 7pm)

Night

(work your way up to dry fasting from the evening until 12pm the following day)

Today's Notes (Highlights, Thoughts, Feelings, What Could You Improve On?)

"Keep your teeth brushed and flossed regularly – at least twice a day to keep them healthy for your fruit sessions. You will notice an improvement in your dental health with this raw/fruit diet."

Today's Date:

Morning

(work towards continuing your night time dry fast up until at least 12pm)

Afternoon

(get hydrating with fresh fruit or even better slow juiced fruits/berries/melons)

Evening

(aim to wind down to a dry fast by around 6pm to 7pm)

Night

(work your way up to dry fasting from the evening until 12pm the following day)

"Be motivated by the vision of becoming an example for others to learn from and follow."

Today's Date:

Morning
(work towards continuing your night time dry fast up until at least 12pm)

Afternoon
(get hydrating with fresh fruit or even better slow juiced fruits/berries/melons)

Evening
(aim to wind down to a dry fast by around 6pm to 7pm)

Night
(work your way up to dry fasting from the evening until 12pm the following day)

Today's Notes (Highlights, Thoughts, Feelings, What Could You Improve On?)

"Embrace your achievements and wonderful results – feel and appreciate the difference within you as a result of this new routine."

Today's Date:

Morning
(work towards continuing your night time dry fast up until at least 12pm)

Afternoon
(get hydrating with fresh fruit or even better slow juiced fruits/berries/melons)

Evening
(aim to wind down to a dry fast by around 6pm to 7pm)

Night
(work your way up to dry fasting from the evening until 12pm the following day)

Today's Notes (Highlights, Thoughts, Feelings, What Could You Improve On?)

"Buy fruit in bulk where possible so you have ample supplies for a week or two in advance. If in a hot climate, you could even freeze your fruit or make ice lollies out of it (crush & freeze)."

Today's Date:

Morning

(work towards continuing your night time dry fast up until at least 12pm)

Afternoon

(get hydrating with fresh fruit or even better slow juiced fruits/berries/melons)

Evening

(aim to wind down to a dry fast by around 6pm to 7pm)

Night

(work your way up to dry fasting from the evening until 12pm the following day)

Today's Notes (Highlights, Thoughts, Feelings, What Could You Improve On?)

"Stay as busy as you can during the daytime. Creating a busy routine makes it easier to manage your diet."

Today's Date:

Morning
(work towards continuing your night time dry fast up until at least 12pm)

Afternoon
(get hydrating with fresh fruit or even better slow juiced fruits/berries/melons)

Evening
(aim to wind down to a dry fast by around 6pm to 7pm)

Night
(work your way up to dry fasting from the evening until 12pm the following day)

Today's Notes (Highlights, Thoughts, Feelings, What Could You Improve On?)

"Complete your fruit and fasting routine with a group of friends/family/colleagues so you can all support one another."

Today's Date:

Morning
(work towards continuing your night time dry fast up until at least 12pm)

Afternoon
(get hydrating with fresh fruit or even better slow juiced fruits/berries/melons)

Evening
(aim to wind down to a dry fast by around 6pm to 7pm)

Night
(work your way up to dry fasting from the evening until 12pm the following day)

"Monitor your urine regularly. Urinate in a jar and leave overnight. If you see a thick cloud of white sediment (success!), your kidneys are filtering acids out."

Today's Date:

Morning

(work towards continuing your night time dry fast up until at least 12pm)

Afternoon

(get hydrating with fresh fruit or even better slow juiced fruits/berries/melons)

Evening

(aim to wind down to a dry fast by around 6pm to 7pm)

Night

(work your way up to dry fasting from the evening until 12pm the following day)

Today's Notes (Highlights, Thoughts, Feelings, What Could You Improve On?)

"Have genuine love and care for yourself. If craving junk food, affirm positive inner talk ("if I eat this, I won't feel good so leave it out")".

Today's Date:

Morning
(work towards continuing your night time dry fast up until at least 12pm)

Afternoon
(get hydrating with fresh fruit or even better slow juiced fruits/berries/melons)

Evening
(aim to wind down to a dry fast by around 6pm to 7pm)

Night
(work your way up to dry fasting from the evening until 12pm the following day)

Today's Notes (Highlights, Thoughts, Feelings, What Could You Improve On?)

"Filter out unwanted acids with this alkaline water-dense fruits protocol."

Today's Date:

Morning
(work towards continuing your night time dry fast up until at least 12pm)

Afternoon
(get hydrating with fresh fruit or even better slow juiced fruits/berries/melons)

Evening
(aim to wind down to a dry fast by around 6pm to 7pm)

Night
(work your way up to dry fasting from the evening until 12pm the following day)

"Look out for white cloud/sediment (acids) in your urine to confirm kidney filtration."

Today's Date:

Morning
(work towards continuing your night time dry fast up until at least 12pm)

Afternoon
(get hydrating with fresh fruit or even better slow juiced fruits/berries/melons)

Evening
(aim to wind down to a dry fast by around 6pm to 7pm)

Night
(work your way up to dry fasting from the evening until 12pm the following day)

Today's Notes (Highlights, Thoughts, Feelings, What Could You Improve On?)

"Infections emerge in an acidic environment"

Today's Date:

Morning

(work towards continuing your night time dry fast up until at least 12pm)

Afternoon

(get hydrating with fresh fruit or even better slow juiced fruits/berries/melons)

Evening

(aim to wind down to a dry fast by around 6pm to 7pm)

Night

(work your way up to dry fasting from the evening until 12pm the following day)

Today's Notes (Highlights, Thoughts, Feelings, What Could You Improve On?)

"Any deficiencies that you may have will disappear once you have cleansed your clogged up gut/colon, kidneys and various other eliminative organs."

Today's Date:

Morning
(work towards continuing your night time dry fast up until at least 12pm)

Afternoon
(get hydrating with fresh fruit or even better slow juiced fruits/berries/melons)

Evening
(aim to wind down to a dry fast by around 6pm to 7pm)

Night
(work your way up to dry fasting from the evening until 12pm the following day)

Today's Notes (Highlights, Thoughts, Feelings, What Could You Improve On?)

"Dependant on how deeply you detox yourself, you could even eliminate any genetic weaknesses that you may have inherited."

Today's Date:

Morning
(work towards continuing your night time dry fast up until at least 12pm)

Afternoon
(get hydrating with fresh fruit or even better slow juiced fruits/berries/melons)

Evening
(aim to wind down to a dry fast by around 6pm to 7pm)

Night
(work your way up to dry fasting from the evening until 12pm the following day)

Today's Notes (Highlights, Thoughts, Feelings, What Could You Improve On?)

"Keep focused on your detox. Even past injuries / trauma are all repairable for good."

Today's Date:

Morning

(work towards continuing your night time dry fast up until at least 12pm)

Afternoon

(get hydrating with fresh fruit or even better slow juiced fruits/berries/melons)

Evening

(aim to wind down to a dry fast by around 6pm to 7pm)

Night

(work your way up to dry fasting from the evening until 12pm the following day)

Today's Notes (Highlights, Thoughts, Feelings, What Could You Improve On?)

"If you suffer from ongoing sadness / depression, a deep detox will support your mental health. You will soon notice a positive change in your mood."

Today's Date:

Morning
(work towards continuing your night time dry fast up until at least 12pm)

Afternoon
(get hydrating with fresh fruit or even better slow juiced fruits/berries/melons)

Evening
(aim to wind down to a dry fast by around 6pm to 7pm)

Night
(work your way up to dry fasting from the evening until 12pm the following day)

"Have your fruits/juices throughout the day. As the evening approaches, start to dry fast – your body wants to rest and heal from this point on."

Today's Date:

Morning
(work towards continuing your night time dry fast up until at least 12pm)

Afternoon
(get hydrating with fresh fruit or even better slow juiced fruits/berries/melons)

Evening
(aim to wind down to a dry fast by around 6pm to 7pm)

Night
(work your way up to dry fasting from the evening until 12pm the following day)

Today's Notes (Highlights, Thoughts, Feelings, What Could You Improve On?)

"The kidneys dislike proteins but really appreciate juicy fruits like melons, berries, citrus fruits, pineapples, mangoes, apples, grapes."

Today's Date:

Morning
(work towards continuing your night time dry fast up until at least 12pm)

Afternoon
(get hydrating with fresh fruit or even better slow juiced fruits/berries/melons)

Evening
(aim to wind down to a dry fast by around 6pm to 7pm)

Night
(work your way up to dry fasting from the evening until 12pm the following day)

Today's Notes (Highlights, Thoughts, Feelings, What Could You Improve On?)

"Healing is very easy. There's no need to complicate it. Keep it simple and you will see results."

Today's Date:

Morning
(work towards continuing your night time dry fast up until at least 12pm)

Afternoon
(get hydrating with fresh fruit or even better slow juiced fruits/berries/melons)

Evening
(aim to wind down to a dry fast by around 6pm to 7pm)

Night
(work your way up to dry fasting from the evening until 12pm the following day)

Today's Notes (Highlights, Thoughts, Feelings, What Could You Improve On?)

"Keep your body in an alkaline state as this is where regeneration takes place."

Today's Date:

Morning
(work towards continuing your night time dry fast up until at least 12pm)

Afternoon
(get hydrating with fresh fruit or even better slow juiced fruits/berries/melons)

Evening
(aim to wind down to a dry fast by around 6pm to 7pm)

Night
(work your way up to dry fasting from the evening until 12pm the following day)

Today's Notes (Highlights, Thoughts, Feelings, What Could You Improve On?)

"A daily enema with boiled water (cooled down) will support your detox greatly."

Today's Date:

Morning

(work towards continuing your night time dry fast up until at least 12pm)

Afternoon

(get hydrating with fresh fruit or even better slow juiced fruits/berries/melons)

Evening

(aim to wind down to a dry fast by around 6pm to 7pm)

Night

(work your way up to dry fasting from the evening until 12pm the following day)

Today's Notes (Highlights, Thoughts, Feelings, What Could You Improve On?)

"*Have your iris' read by an iridologist that works with Dr Bernard Jensen's system.*"

Today's Date:

Morning
(work towards continuing your night time dry fast up until at least 12pm)

Afternoon
(get hydrating with fresh fruit or even better slow juiced fruits/berries/melons)

Evening
(aim to wind down to a dry fast by around 6pm to 7pm)

Night
(work your way up to dry fasting from the evening until 12pm the following day)

Today's Notes (Highlights, Thoughts, Feelings, What Could You Improve On?)

"Take a herbal parasite formula for a month. It will eliminate food cravings. This is an important point."

Today's Date:

Morning
(work towards continuing your night time dry fast up until at least 12pm)

Afternoon
(get hydrating with fresh fruit or even better slow juiced fruits/berries/melons)

Evening
(aim to wind down to a dry fast by around 6pm to 7pm)

Night
(work your way up to dry fasting from the evening until 12pm the following day)

Today's Notes (Highlights, Thoughts, Feelings, What Could You Improve On?)

"Your skin is the largest eliminative organ. Skin brushing and sweating are crucial. Sauna heat is ideal, steam can also work."

Today's Date:

Morning
(work towards continuing your night time dry fast up until at least 12pm)

Afternoon
(get hydrating with fresh fruit or even better slow juiced fruits/berries/melons)

Evening
(aim to wind down to a dry fast by around 6pm to 7pm)

Night
(work your way up to dry fasting from the evening until 12pm the following day)

Today's Notes (Highlights, Thoughts, Feelings, What Could You Improve On?)

"If you are on medications, monitor the relevant statistics (e.g. blood pressure, blood sugar level, etc). Upon improving, lower medication"

Today's Date:

Morning
(work towards continuing your night time dry fast up until at least 12pm)

Afternoon
(get hydrating with fresh fruit or even better slow juiced fruits/berries/melons)

Evening
(aim to wind down to a dry fast by around 6pm to 7pm)

Night
(work your way up to dry fasting from the evening until 12pm the following day)

Today's Notes (Highlights, Thoughts, Feelings, What Could You Improve On?)

"Most people do not breathe effectively. Your body requires a healthy supply of oxygen to heal. Practice breathing techniques daily."

Today's Date:

Morning

(work towards continuing your night time dry fast up until at least 12pm)

Afternoon

(get hydrating with fresh fruit or even better slow juiced fruits/berries/melons)

Evening

(aim to wind down to a dry fast by around 6pm to 7pm)

Night

(work your way up to dry fasting from the evening until 12pm the following day)

Today's Notes (Highlights, Thoughts, Feelings, What Could You Improve On?)

"Disease is not the presence of something evil, but rather the lack of the presence of something essential."
— Dr. Bernard Jensen.

Today's Date:

Morning
(work towards continuing your night time dry fast up until at least 12pm)

Afternoon
(get hydrating with fresh fruit or even better slow juiced fruits/berries/melons)

Evening
(aim to wind down to a dry fast by around 6pm to 7pm)

Night
(work your way up to dry fasting from the evening until 12pm the following day)

Today's Notes (Highlights, Thoughts, Feelings, What Could You Improve On?)

"Fruits will empower you, providing live energy. Cooked foods in comparison will use vital energy that could otherwise be used for healing."

Today's Date:

Morning
(work towards continuing your night time dry fast up until at least 12pm)

Afternoon
(get hydrating with fresh fruit or even better slow juiced fruits/berries/melons)

Evening
(aim to wind down to a dry fast by around 6pm to 7pm)

Night
(work your way up to dry fasting from the evening until 12pm the following day)

Today's Notes (Highlights, Thoughts, Feelings, What Could You Improve On?)

"Fructose (the sugar found in fruits) is kind to the pancreas and its absorption into the body uses minimal energy."

Today's Date:

Morning

(work towards continuing your night time dry fast up until at least 12pm)

Afternoon

(get hydrating with fresh fruit or even better slow juiced fruits/berries/melons)

Evening

(aim to wind down to a dry fast by around 6pm to 7pm)

Night

(work your way up to dry fasting from the evening until 12pm the following day)

Today's Notes (Highlights, Thoughts, Feelings, What Could You Improve On?)

"*Fruits have the highest healing energy frequencies among all food groups. Vegetables are the next highest. Cooked meats rank the lowest.*"

Today's Date:

Morning

(work towards continuing your night time dry fast up until at least 12pm)

Afternoon

(get hydrating with fresh fruit or even better slow juiced fruits/berries/melons)

Evening

(aim to wind down to a dry fast by around 6pm to 7pm)

Night

(work your way up to dry fasting from the evening until 12pm the following day)

Today's Notes (Highlights, Thoughts, Feelings, What Could You Improve On?)

"Mucus congestion (caused by dairy products) leads to a lack of mineral utilization (Calcium, Magnesium, Potassium, etc)."

Today's Date:

Morning
(work towards continuing your night time dry fast up until at least 12pm)

Afternoon
(get hydrating with fresh fruit or even better slow juiced fruits/berries/melons)

Evening
(aim to wind down to a dry fast by around 6pm to 7pm)

Night
(work your way up to dry fasting from the evening until 12pm the following day)

Today's Notes (Highlights, Thoughts, Feelings, What Could You Improve On?)

"Did you know that fruit juice (slow juiced) will offer you more Calcium than Cow's Milk?"

Today's Date:

Morning
(work towards continuing your night time dry fast up until at least 12pm)

Afternoon
(get hydrating with fresh fruit or even better slow juiced fruits/berries/melons)

Evening
(aim to wind down to a dry fast by around 6pm to 7pm)

Night
(work your way up to dry fasting from the evening until 12pm the following day)

"Your body will use sweating (fevers), vomiting, diarrhea, frequent urination, colds, flus, and daily elimination as means to detox a toxic state. Let it run its course."

Today's Date:

Morning
(work towards continuing your night time dry fast up until at least 12pm)

Afternoon
(get hydrating with fresh fruit or even better slow juiced fruits/berries/melons)

Evening
(aim to wind down to a dry fast by around 6pm to 7pm)

Night
(work your way up to dry fasting from the evening until 12pm the following day)

Today's Notes (Highlights, Thoughts, Feelings, What Could You Improve On?)

"Pain is merely a sign of energy blockage(s) resulting from acidosis. Alkalization is the key (through detoxification)."

Today's Date:

Morning
(work towards continuing your night time dry fast up until at least 12pm)

Afternoon
(get hydrating with fresh fruit or even better slow juiced fruits/berries/melons)

Evening
(aim to wind down to a dry fast by around 6pm to 7pm)

Night
(work your way up to dry fasting from the evening until 12pm the following day)

Today's Notes (Highlights, Thoughts, Feelings, What Could You Improve On?)

"Keep on loving! Love is alkalizing,
it improves digestion and kidney
elimination. Your blood and lymph flow
will also improve."

Today's Date:

Morning
(work towards continuing your night time dry fast up until at least 12pm)

Afternoon
(get hydrating with fresh fruit or even better slow juiced fruits/berries/melons)

Evening
(aim to wind down to a dry fast by around 6pm to 7pm)

Night
(work your way up to dry fasting from the evening until 12pm the following day)

Today's Notes (Highlights, Thoughts, Feelings, What Could You Improve On?)

"*Ensure any amalgam fillings in your teeth are replaced with composite fillings – preferably by a holistic dentist.*"

Today's Date:

Morning
(work towards continuing your night time dry fast up until at least 12pm)

Afternoon
(get hydrating with fresh fruit or even better slow juiced fruits/berries/melons)

Evening
(aim to wind down to a dry fast by around 6pm to 7pm)

Night
(work your way up to dry fasting from the evening until 12pm the following day)

Today's Notes (Highlights, Thoughts, Feelings, What Could You Improve On?)

"Use parsley to detox mercury out of your body."

Today's Date:

Morning
(work towards continuing your night time dry fast up until at least 12pm)

Afternoon
(get hydrating with fresh fruit or even better slow juiced fruits/berries/melons)

Evening
(aim to wind down to a dry fast by around 6pm to 7pm)

Night
(work your way up to dry fasting from the evening until 12pm the following day)

Today's Notes (Highlights, Thoughts, Feelings, What Could You Improve On?)

"Sleep is very vital for your healing. Wind down by 7pm and aim to be in bed by 10pm to 10:30pm (if possible)."

Today's Date:

Morning
(work towards continuing your night time dry fast up until at least 12pm)

Afternoon
(get hydrating with fresh fruit or even better slow juiced fruits/berries/melons)

Evening
(aim to wind down to a dry fast by around 6pm to 7pm)

Night
(work your way up to dry fasting from the evening until 12pm the following day)

Today's Notes (Highlights, Thoughts, Feelings, What Could You Improve On?)

"Keep a positive mindset. Remind yourself that everything is possible & you WILL achieve your goals"

CPSIA information can be obtained
at www.ICGtesting.com
Printed in the USA
LVHW082146240319
611697LV00025B/493/P

9 781395 272630